Contents

Welcome! 3

Unit 1: Weather 7

Unit 2: Journeys 12

Unit 3: Fox at the Farm 17

Unit 4: Fun at the Fair 22

Unit 5: At the Castle 27

Unit 6: A Camping Trip 32

Unit 7: Doctor, Doctor! 37

Unit 8: A Party 42

Vocabulary Review 47

  # Welcome!

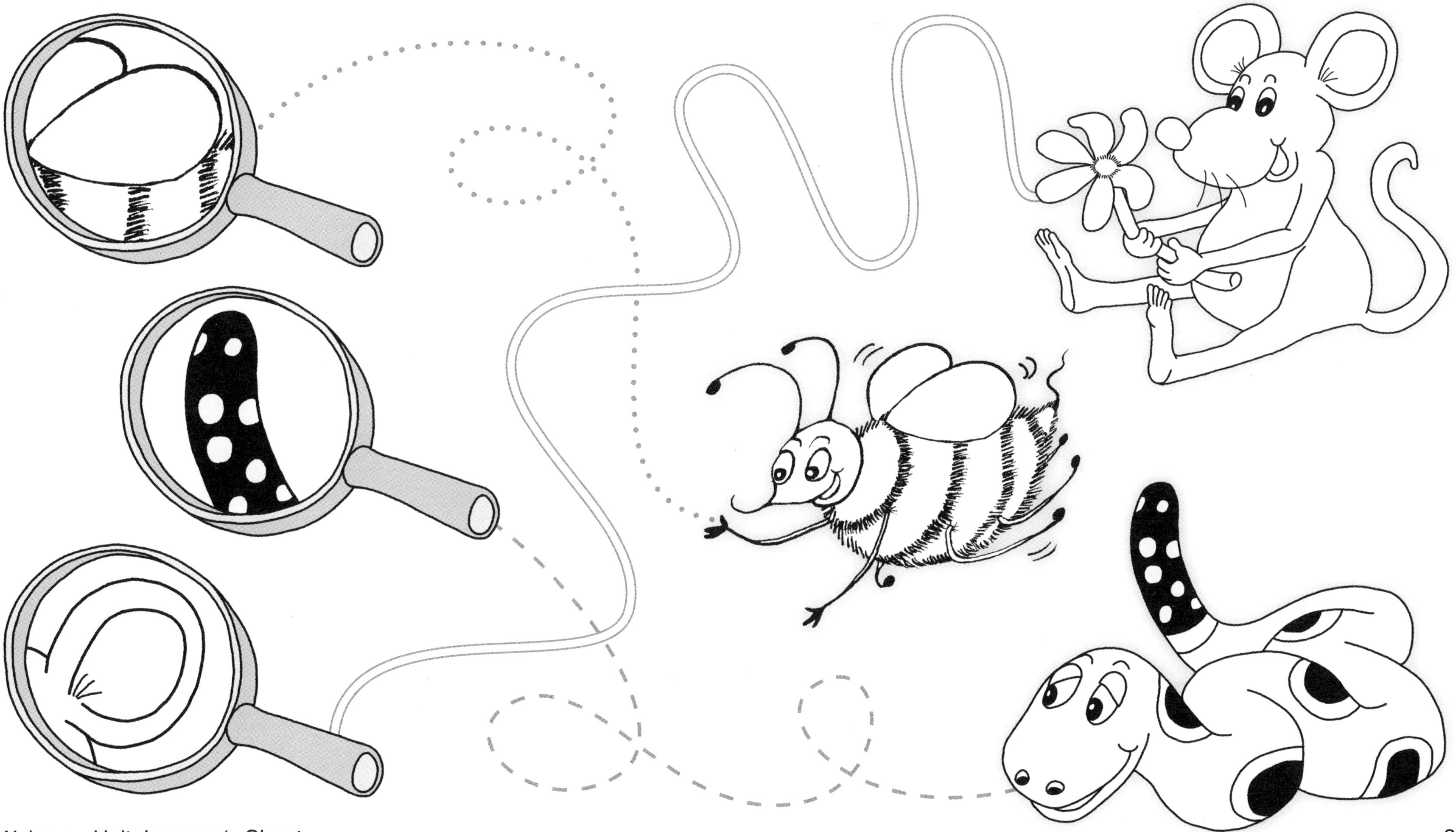

Welcome Unit, Lesson 1: Chant

3

Welcome Unit, Lesson 4: Vocabulary

Unit 1, Lesson 1: Vocabulary

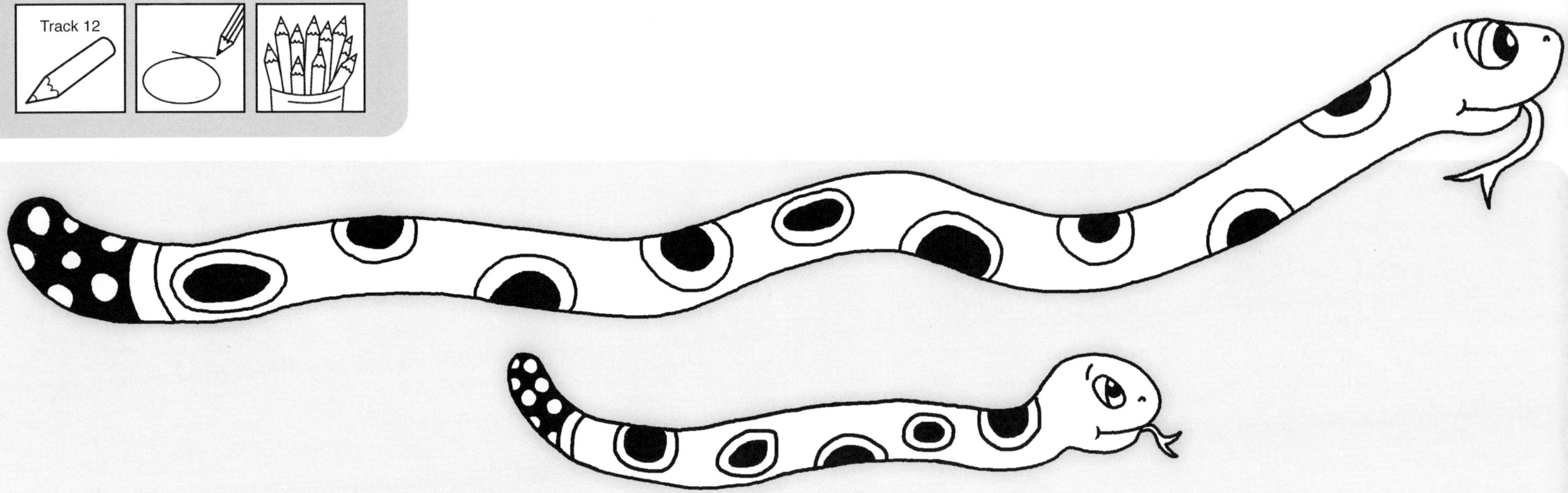

Unit 1, Lesson 2: Vocabulary

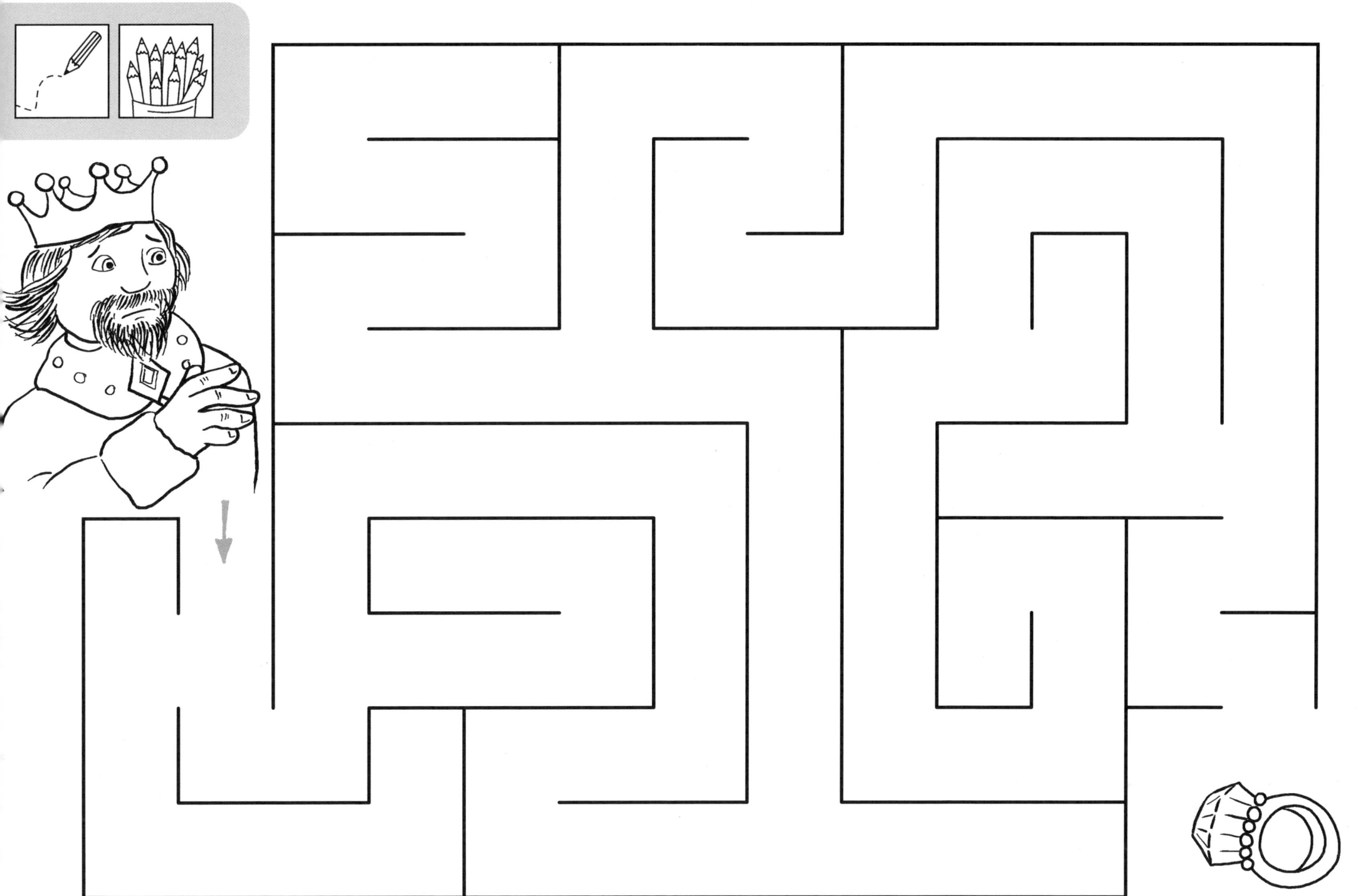

Unit 1, Lesson 3: Story

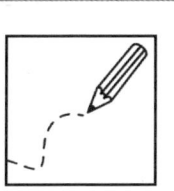

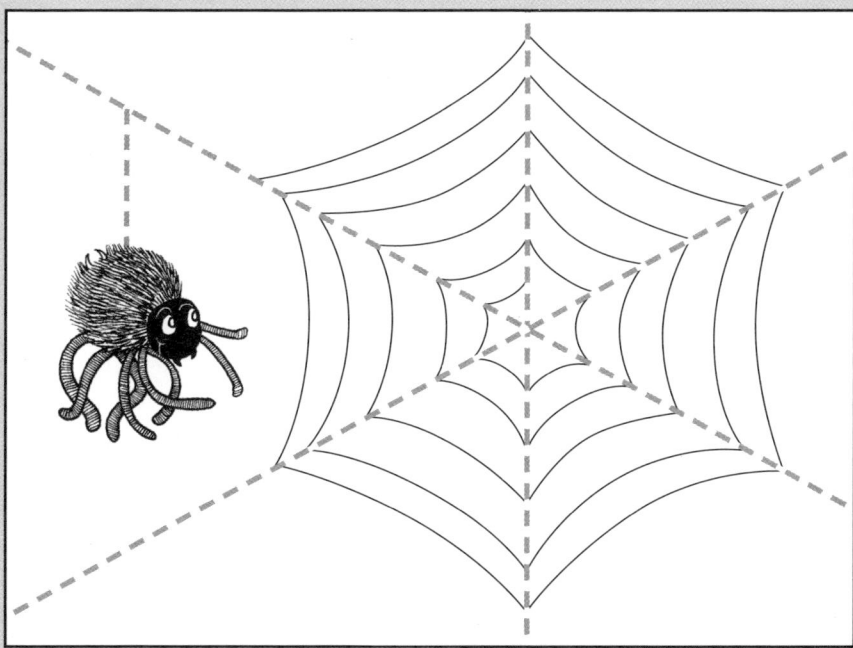

Review 1: /w/, /ng/

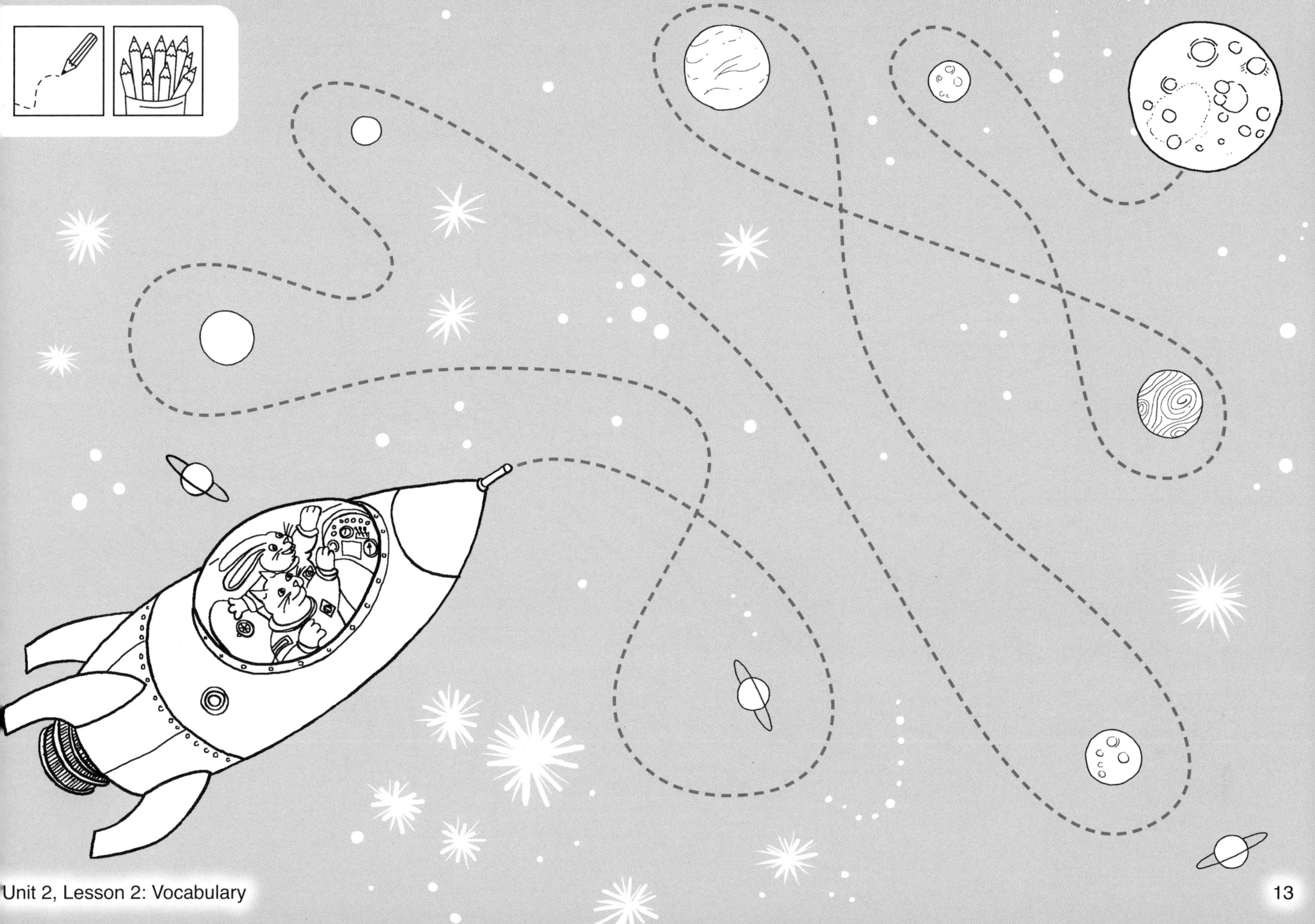

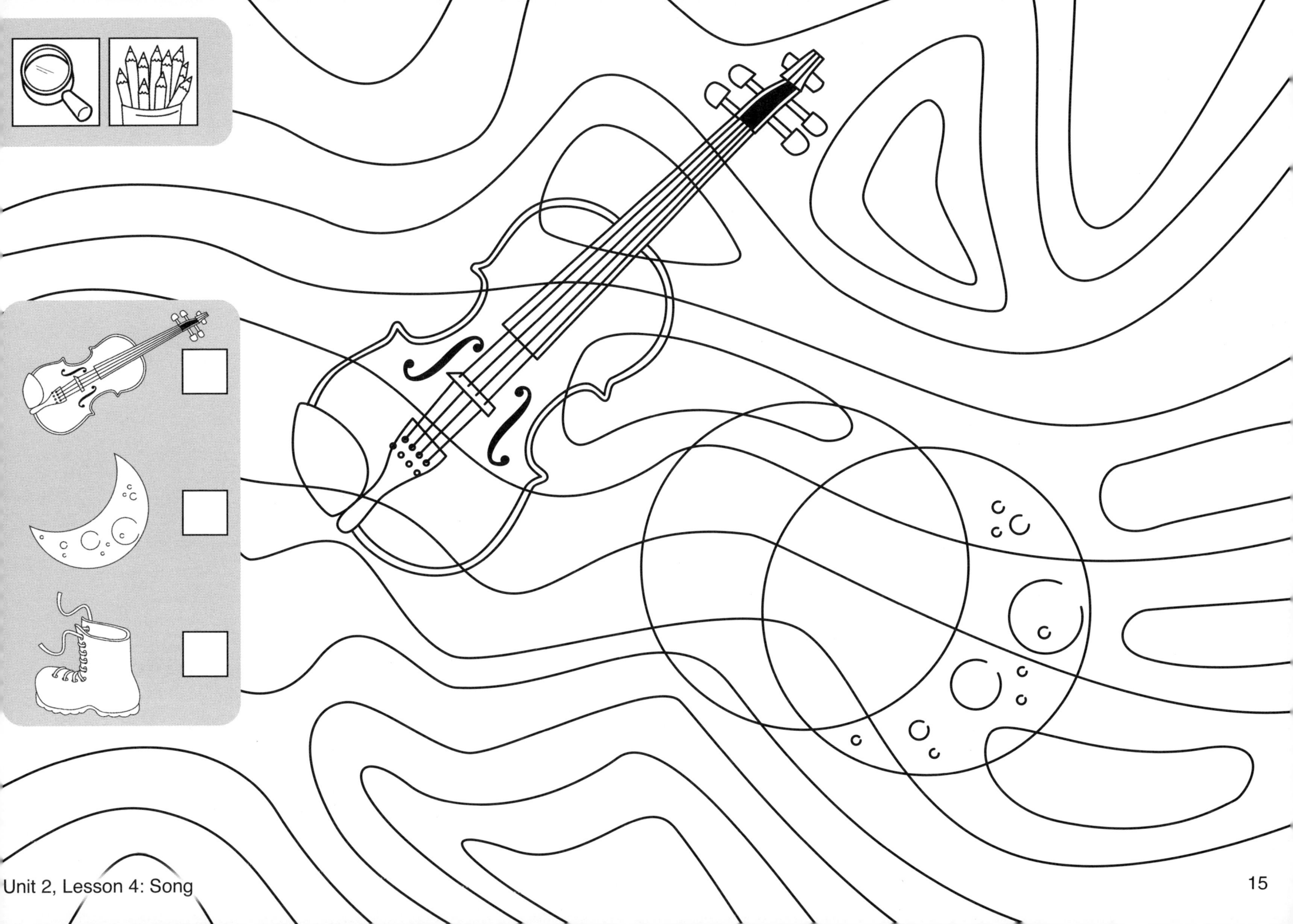

Review 2: /v/, /oo/, /oo/

Fox at the Farm

Unit 3, Lesson 1: Vocabulary

Unit 3, Lesson 3: Story

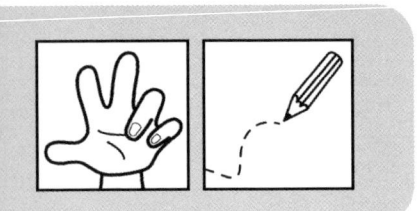

Unit 3, Lesson 4: Song

Review 3: /y/, /x/, /ch/

Fun at the Fair

 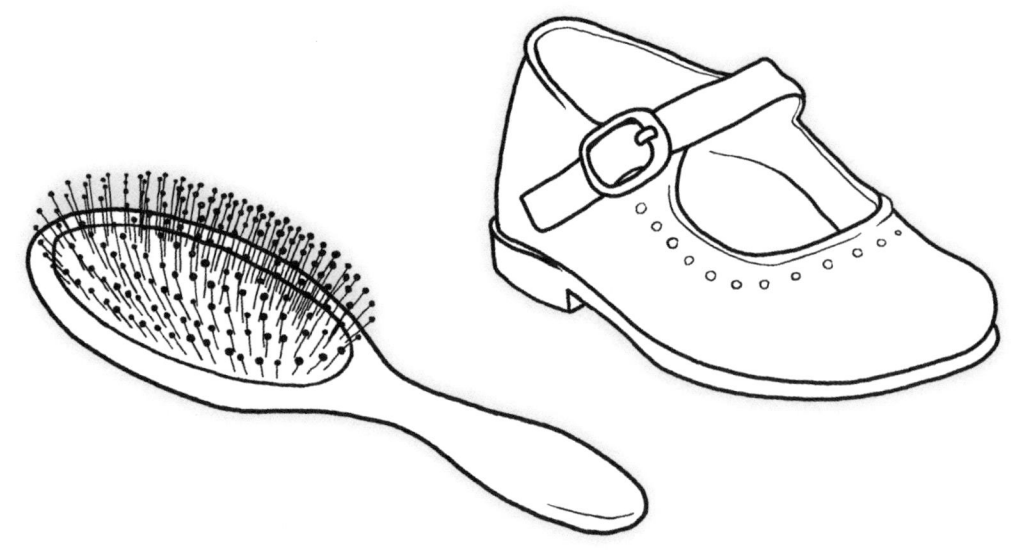 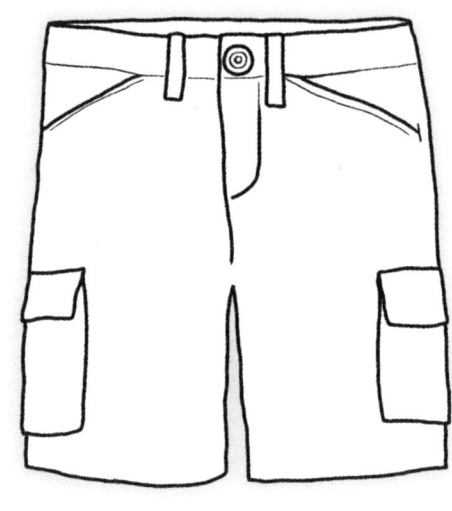

  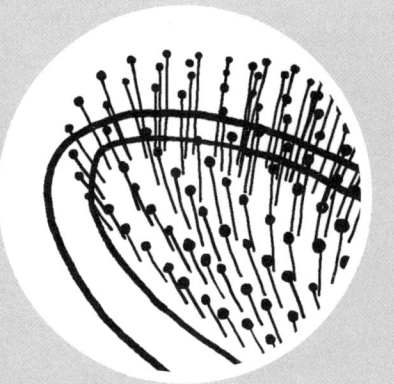 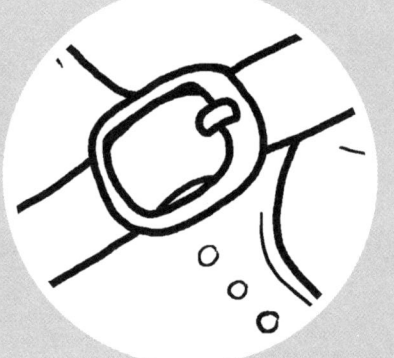

Unit 4, Lesson 1: Vocabulary

Unit 4, Lesson 2: Vocabulary

Unit 4, Lesson 4: Song

Review 4: /sh/, /th/, /th/

At the Castle

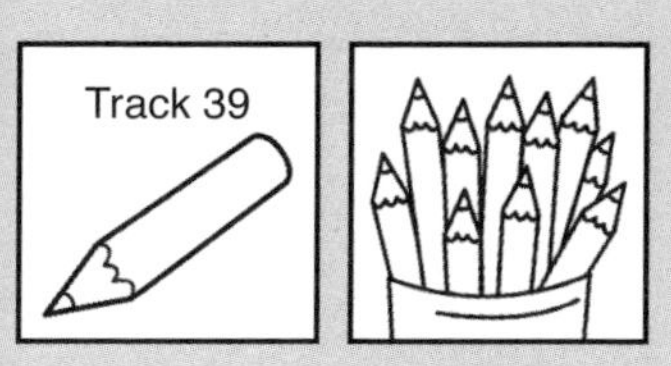

Unit 5, Lesson 1: Vocabulary

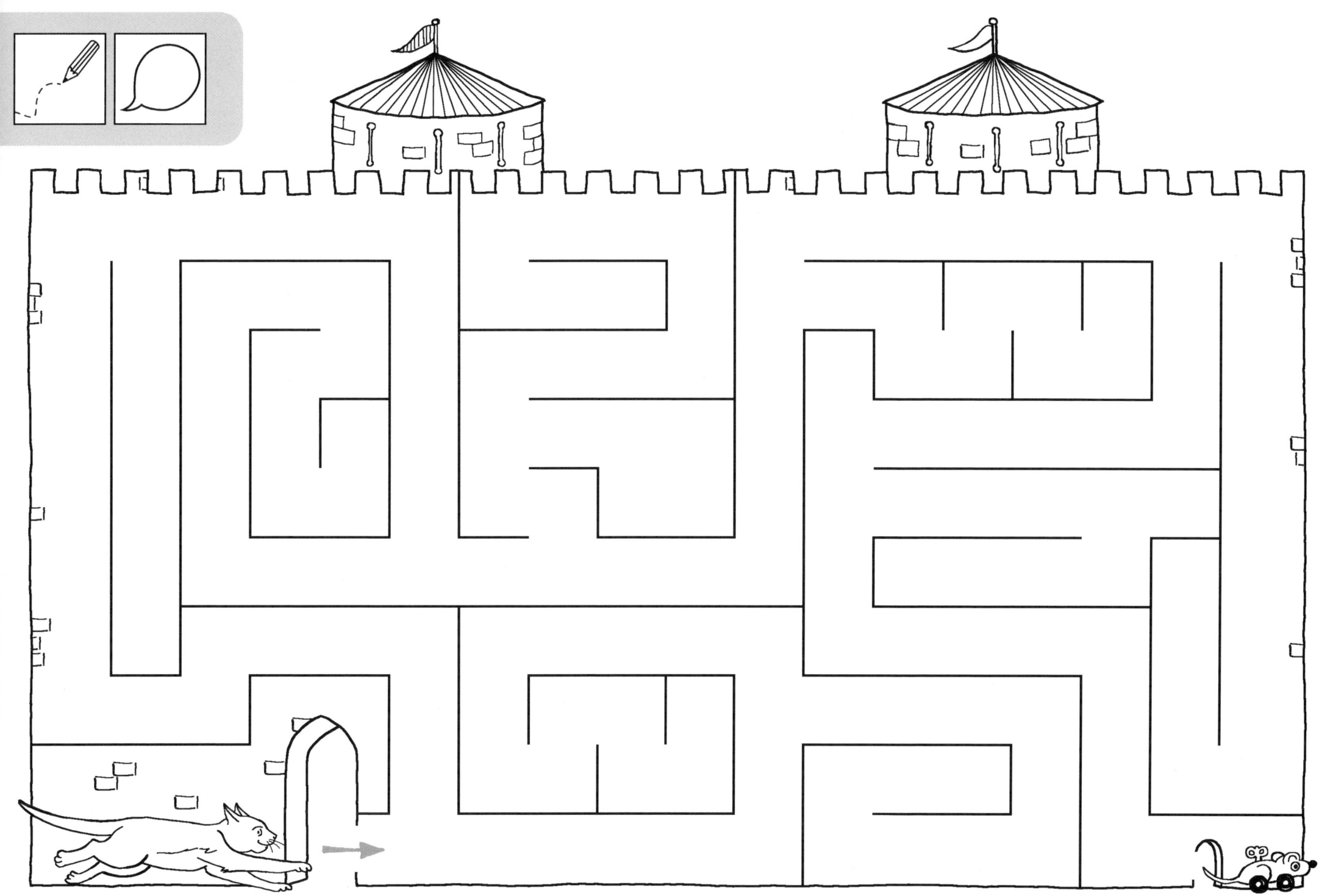

Review 5: /qu/, /ou/, /oi/

A Camping Trip

Unit 6, Lesson 1: Vocabulary

Unit 6, Lesson 2: Vocabulary

Unit 6, Lesson 4: Song

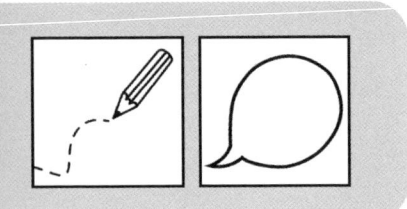

Review 6: /ue/, /er/, /ar/

Doctor, Doctor!

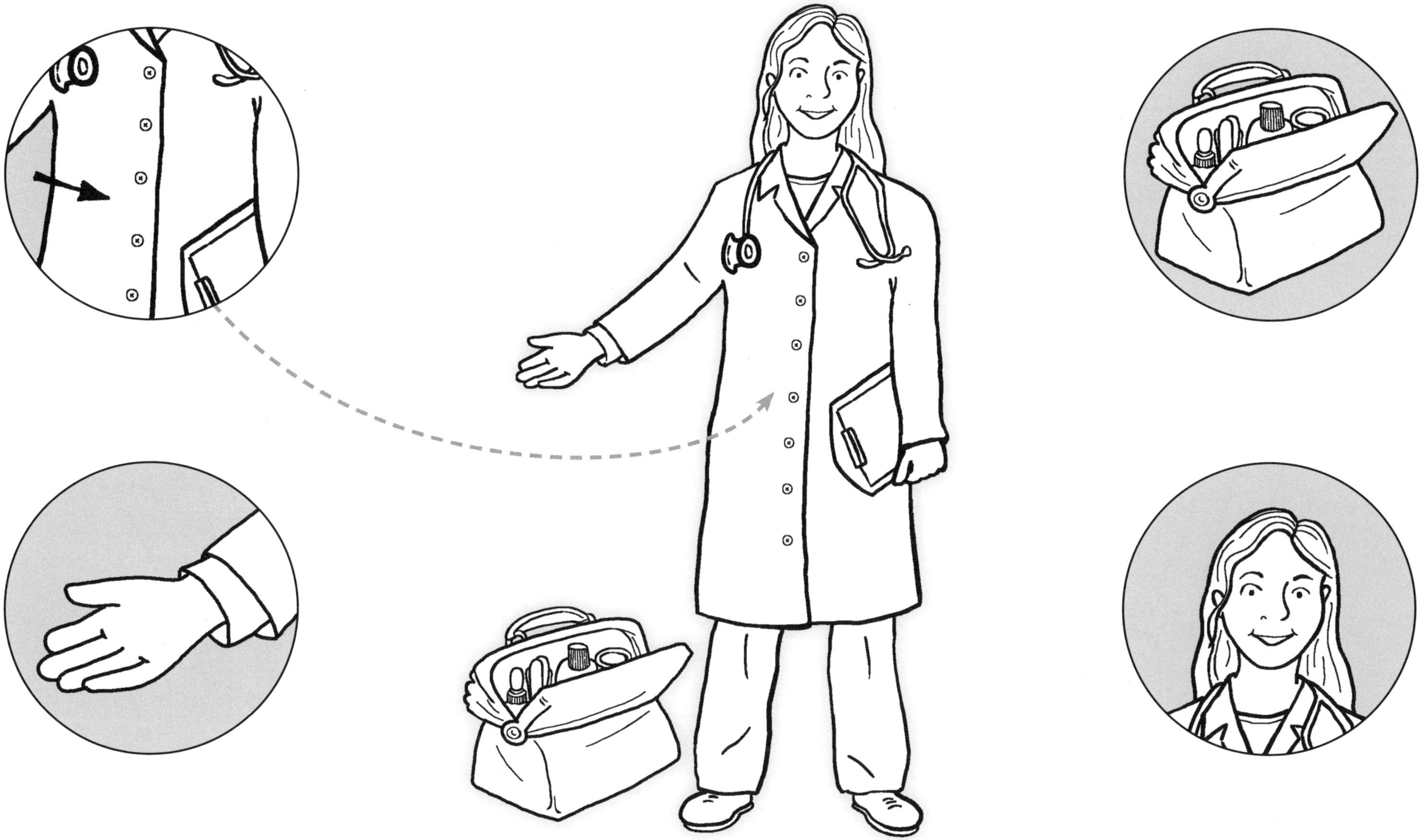

Unit 7, Lesson 1: Vocabulary

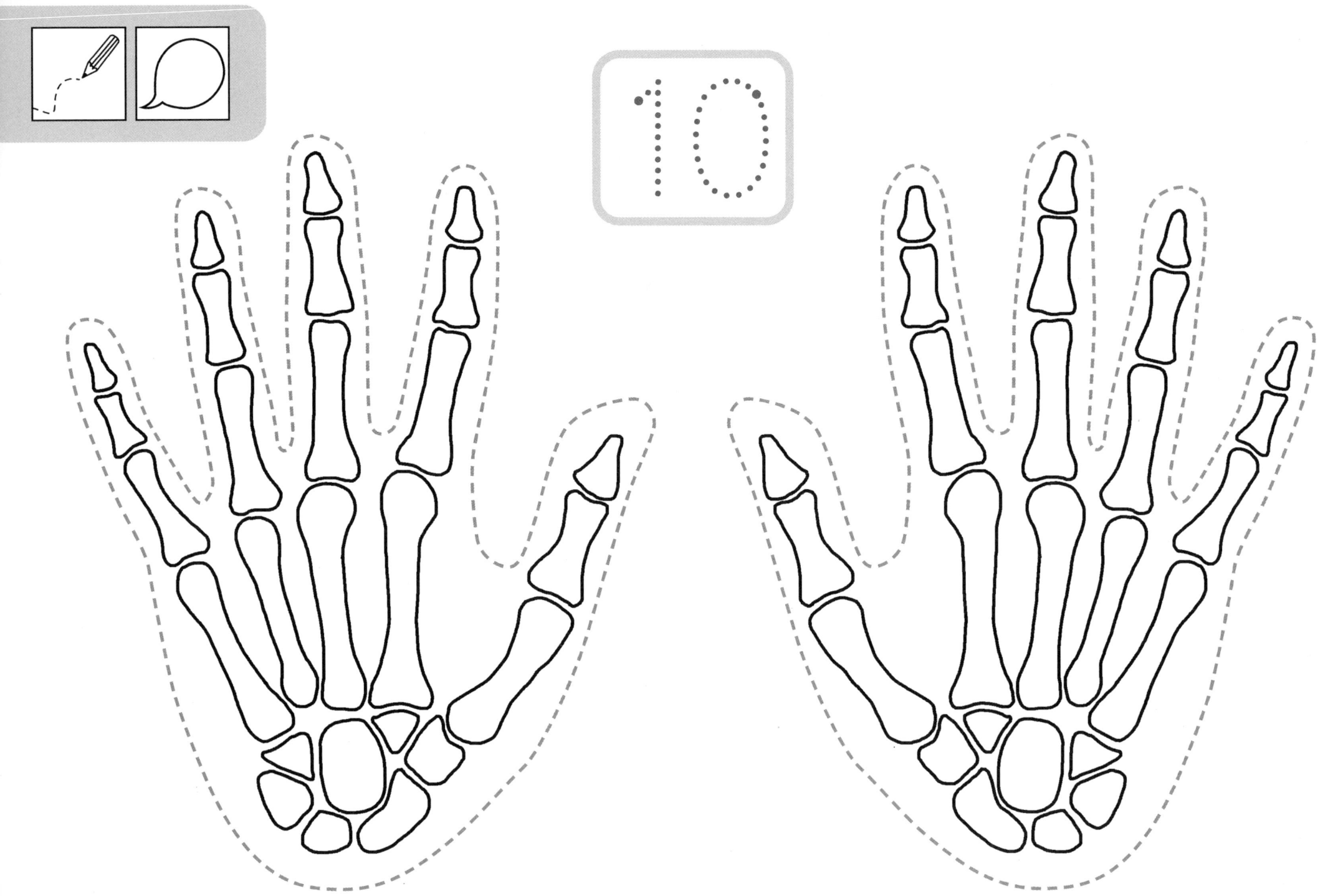

Unit 7, Lesson 3: Story

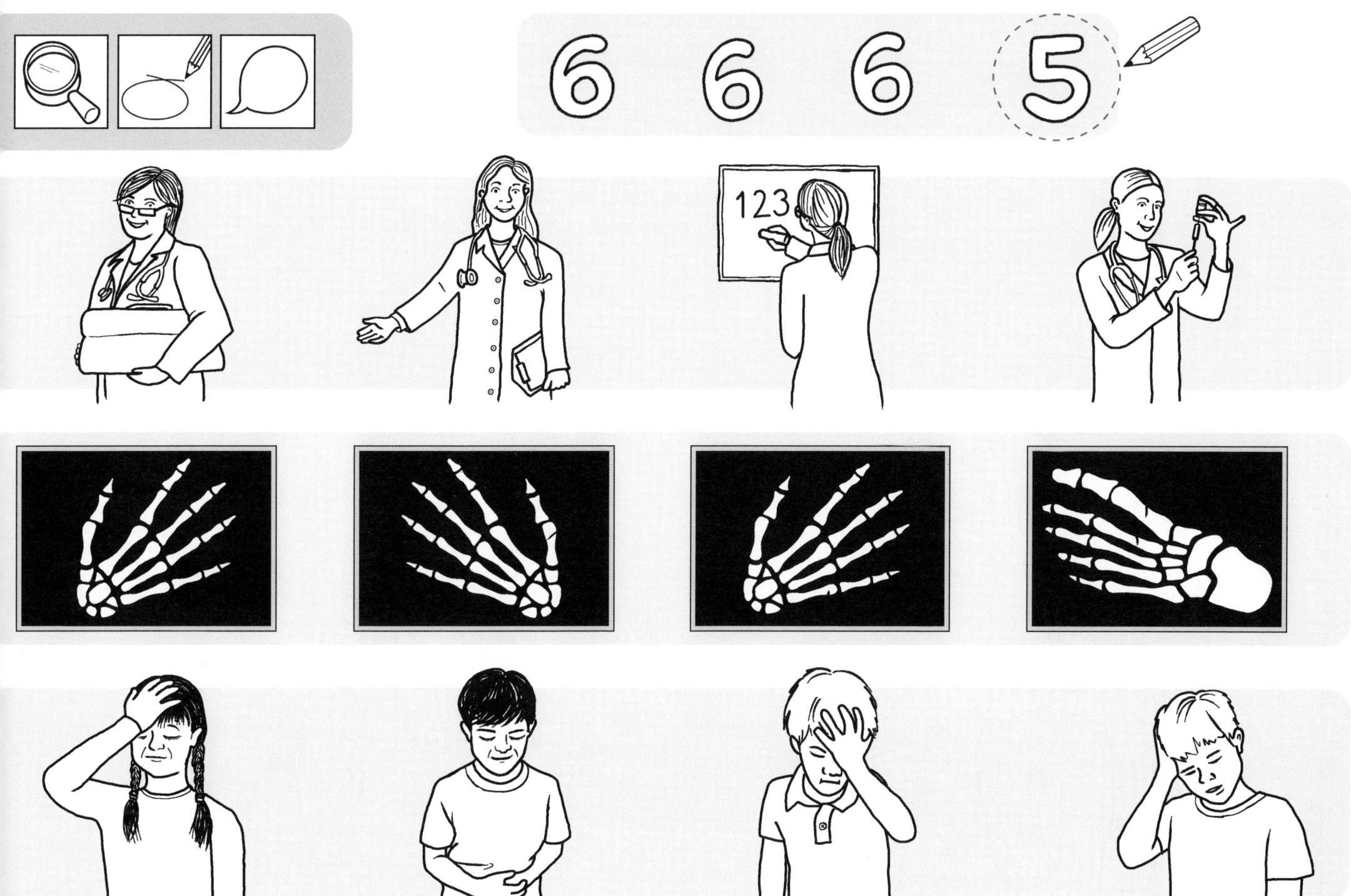

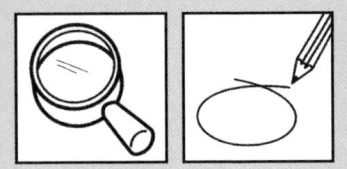
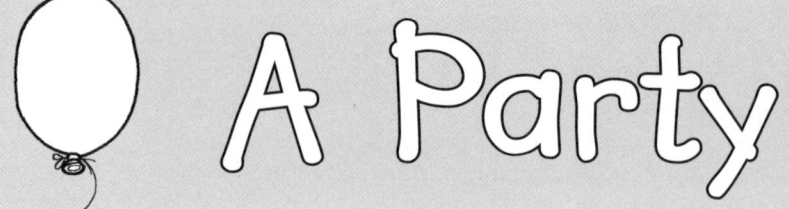

A Party

Unit 8, Lesson 2: Vocabulary

43

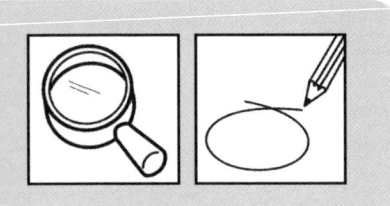

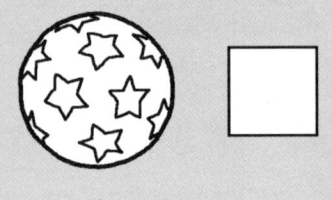

46

Review 8: /ou/, /t/, /ue.

Vocabulary Review

Weather

Clothing

1 2 3 4 5 6 7 8 9 10

House and garden

48 Vocabulary review